TALES FROM THE GREEK MYTHS

Orpheus and Eurydice

Calliope Kyrdi
Illustrated by Sandra Eleftheriou

Translated by Leo Kalovyrnas

METAICHMIO ⊕

1st edition April 2018

ORIGINAL TITLE Καλλιόπη Κύρδη,
Ορφέας και Ευρυδίκη, Μεταίχμιο 2016

TRANSLATED FROM THE GREEK LANGUAGE BY Leo Kalovyrnas
ILLUSTRATED BY Sandra Eleftheriou

ISBN 978-618-03-1455-7
AUXIL. COMPU. CODE 81455
C.E.P. 4338 C.P. 9748

© 2017 METAICHMIO Publications
and Calliope Kyrdi

Bookstores
1. 18 ASKLIPIOU STR., 106 80 ATHENS
TEL. +30 210 3647433, FAX: +30 211 3003562
Internet Site: www.metaixmio.gr
e-mail: metaixmio@metaixmio.gr

2. POLYCHOROS, 118 IPPOKRATOUS STR., 114 72 ATHENS
TEL. +30 210 3003580, FAX: +30 211 3003581

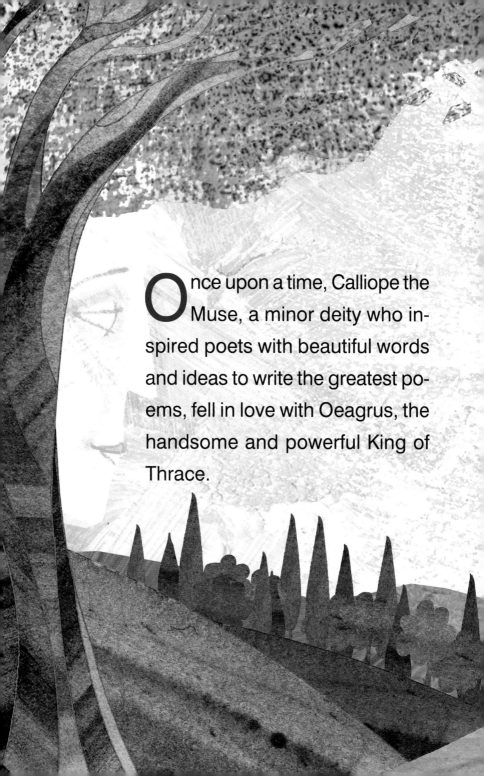

Once upon a time, Calliope the Muse, a minor deity who inspired poets with beautiful words and ideas to write the greatest poems, fell in love with Oeagrus, the handsome and powerful King of Thrace.

For Aggeliki & Damianos,
who no longer believe in fairytales.

C.K.

They had a love child, Orpheus, who grew up in the leafy forests and evergreen mountains of Thrace.

Now Orpheus was a child blessed by the Fates with many gifts and talents. He listened to the wind, the waves, the rustling leaves, the birdsong, and all the secret sounds of nature and turned everything into enchanting melodies. His music brimmed with light and entranced both animals and humans, for it healed all sorrows.

Even the little gods of the trees and flowers, of the springs and the winds fell under the spell of his music. Mighty winds and soft breezes, babbling brooks and gushing torrents, reeds and leaves, and all the birds gladly changed their sounds to accompany Orpheus's melodies. Even the wild beasts, the unyielding rocks, and the ancient deep-rooted trees were so deeply moved by his music that they gathered closer to hear him play the lyre.

Just like all exceptional young men in the olden days, Orpheus went on a quest. He travelled together with Jason and the Argonauts to the far end of the Black Sea to bring back the Golden Fleece, but that is another story.

And then one day he fell in love. He fell madly in love. His sweetheart's name was Euridice. They got married and were truly happy. But like in most stories of yesteryear, happiness was never meant to last long.

One day, Euridice and her friends, the woodland and water nymphs, went to gather flowers that could match her joy. Unfortunately, she accidentally stepped on a venomous snake that lay coiled up in the high grass. At once the light went out in Euridice's eyes, and her soul travelled to the Underworld, where everything is bleak and dark.

The light went out in Orpheus's music, too, and his tunes turned into misery and despair.

'Either I'll bring her back from the darkness of death,' he vowed, 'or I shall perish, too. I am going to journey forth to the Underworld and I'm going to ask Pluto, the lord

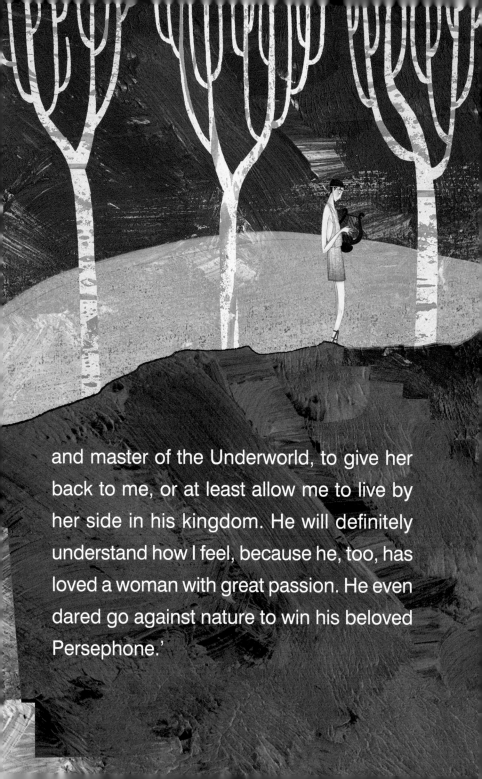

and master of the Underworld, to give her back to me, or at least allow me to live by her side in his kingdom. He will definitely understand how I feel, because he, too, has loved a woman with great passion. He even dared go against nature to win his beloved Persephone.'

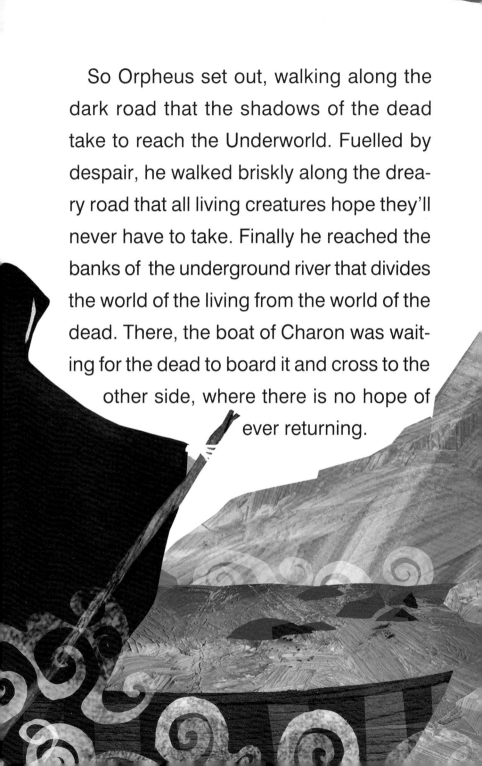

So Orpheus set out, walking along the dark road that the shadows of the dead take to reach the Underworld. Fuelled by despair, he walked briskly along the dreary road that all living creatures hope they'll never have to take. Finally he reached the banks of the underground river that divides the world of the living from the world of the dead. There, the boat of Charon was waiting for the dead to board it and cross to the other side, where there is no hope of ever returning.

'I have strict orders from my master, Lord Pluto, to not allow a living being on my boat,' said the ferryman of the dead to Orpheus.

'Since the day Euridice died I am as good as dead myself,' said Orpheus and began to play a lovesick song on his lyre.

Mesmerised by Orpheus's music, Charon allowed him on his boat and ferried him across the river, there where darkness ruled supreme.

The creatures of the Netherworld that had been mournfully moaning and groaning immediately fell silent and began to hum Orpheus's melodies. Even Cerberus, the monstrous three-headed dog that stood guard at the gate to the realm of Death, bent his heads and wagged his three tails, stepping aside to let Orpheus through. And all this happened because his songs were brimming with so much love that there was

enough love to go around for all creatures, both in the world of the living and the world of the dead.

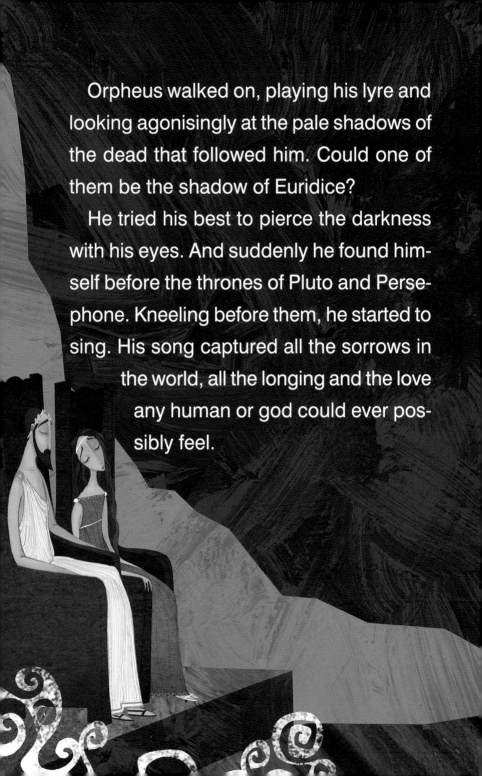

Orpheus walked on, playing his lyre and looking agonisingly at the pale shadows of the dead that followed him. Could one of them be the shadow of Euridice?

He tried his best to pierce the darkness with his eyes. And suddenly he found himself before the thrones of Pluto and Persephone. Kneeling before them, he started to sing. His song captured all the sorrows in the world, all the longing and the love any human or god could ever possibly feel.

His music touched the regal pair deeply, warming their hearts. For the first time in their lives, Pluto and Persephone felt hope steal into their world.

They were reminded of how they were forced to part ways every year, when Persephone had to travel up to the earth's surface to bring springtime. However, both Pluto and Persephone knew that even though they had to part, there would soon come a time when they'd meet again, whereas Orpheus would have to wait to die before he could see his beloved Persephone again. And so they made their decision.

'I don't have the power to keep you here so that you may be with your sweetheart. I rule over the dead, so I have no authority over you,' said Pluto. 'But for the first and only one time I am going to allow a dead person to leave the Underworld, and that dead person is Euridice. This is how it'll be done. You are going to walk out of here, and she is going to follow you. But beware! As long as you are in my kingdom you must not turn to look back. Don't turn to check if she's following you, for if you do, she will vanish. You are to walk out, following Hermes's footsteps, whom I have asked to show you the way out. Only when you see the blue sky again and feel the warmth of the sun's rays, only when the green grass tickles your feet and you hear the birds chirping, only when the darkness is well and true behind you, should you turn around and hug your precious Euridice.'

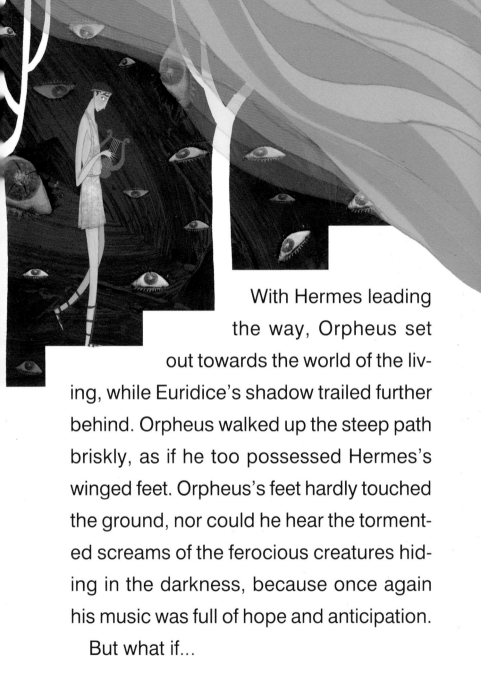

With Hermes leading the way, Orpheus set out towards the world of the living, while Euridice's shadow trailed further behind. Orpheus walked up the steep path briskly, as if he too possessed Hermes's winged feet. Orpheus's feet hardly touched the ground, nor could he hear the tormented screams of the ferocious creatures hiding in the darkness, because once again his music was full of hope and anticipation.

But what if...

What if Euridice lost their trail at some bend of the path? What if she tripped on a rock? What if she was terrified out of her wits? Shouldn't he just turn his head just a little to catch a quick glimpse? No, he had taken a vow not to.

Orpheus continued wending his way out of the Underworld troubled by worrying thoughts until at long last he caught sight of daylight far in the distance. The further he walked on the stronger the light grew. It was the sun waiting for them, and soon they'd be in each other's arms again. He halted for a moment to hear her footsteps and rally his courage for the last few remaining yards. But all he heard was absolute silence. What if Euridice had got lost? Orpheus turned his head to look. He caught sight of her shadow, but immediately she started

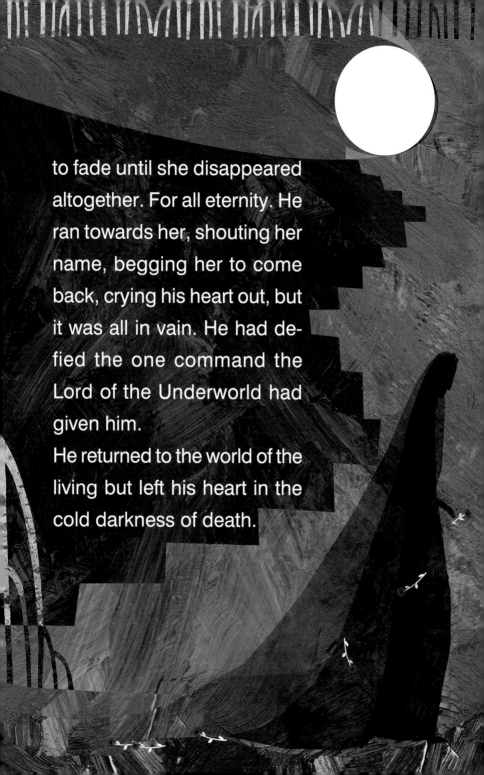

to fade until she disappeared altogether. For all eternity. He ran towards her, shouting her name, begging her to come back, crying his heart out, but it was all in vain. He had defied the one command the Lord of the Underworld had given him.

He returned to the world of the living but left his heart in the cold darkness of death.

Orpheus wandered aimlessly among the shadows in the woods, playing laments that brought tears to everyone's eyes. Anyone who happened to hear his music was overcome with a wish to make it their own. Orpheus drifted as if in a dream, his mind riveted to the shadow of his beloved Euridice, who had been lost forever between light and darkness. He was so distracted that he didn't hear voices calling him to play his lyre for a dance. It was the voices of women who were celebrating in honour of the god of wine, Dionysus. Orpheus barely noticed them, even though he passed right by them. The women pounced on him, to claim his music as their own. It was there that Orpheus breathed his last breath, plucking his lyre for the very last time. He could finally join his sweetheart in the Land of Shadows.

PLAYING
WITH THE
MYTH

Educational material
by Maria Gonidaki

ORPHEUS AND EURIDICE

According to the most well-known version of the myth, Orpheus was the son of the king of Thrace Oeagrus and the Muse of epic poetry Calliope. He learnt everything there is to know about music from god Apollo (who in another version of the myth is said to be his father). Apollo also gave him a lyre as a present.

Orpheus was a famous singer. Each time he sang and played his lyre he moved not only humans, but every living creature; wild animals grew tame, and birds and fish drew near to listen to him. His music was so wonderful that even the trees would bend towards him.

It was Orpheus's gift of music that convinced Jason to take him along on the Expedition of the Argonauts. Orpheus was tasked with giving rhythm to the oarsmen of Argo, taming the waves, and lulling to sleep the dragon that guarded the Golden Fleece. It was also thanks to his enchanting song that the Argonauts managed to ignore the singing of the Sirens and sail past their island unscathed.

But his singing did not charm only the living; even the dead were enthralled by his melodies. When he travelled deep into Hades to bring back his beloved Euridice, who had died an untimely death after being bitten by a snake, his music tamed the formidable three-headed Cerberus. His music also put a stop to the tortures inflicted on the wicked dead. Yet it wasn't just Orpheus's singing that convinced Pluto and Persephone to allow Euridice to return to the land of the living, a feat no mortal had ever accomplished. It was Orpheus's profound love for her, which he poured into his music. Unfortunately, it was this same love that stopped Orpheus from obeying the one and only condition that Pluto had imposed: to not turn his head to see if Euridice was following until after they stood in broad daylight again. Orpheus could not stop himself from turning and when he did, she was gone forever.

There were no words to describe Orpheus's pain. He stopped singing and cried and cried till there were no tears left. According to one version of the myth, he even neglected to worship Dionysus, and so the god punished him by having his Maenads, the female worshippers who followed Dionysus, slay him.

WORD GAME

▶ Fill in the missing words and the name of Orpheus's mother will appear vertically.

1. Oeagrus was king of …
2. The name of the Underworld.
3. The one who gave Orpheus the lyre.
4. Orpheus helped the Argonauts retrieve the Golden …
5. Orpheus's sweetheart was called…
6. The name of the ferryman of the dead.
7. Pluto's wife was called…
8. This god showed Euridice and Orpheus the way out of the Underworld.

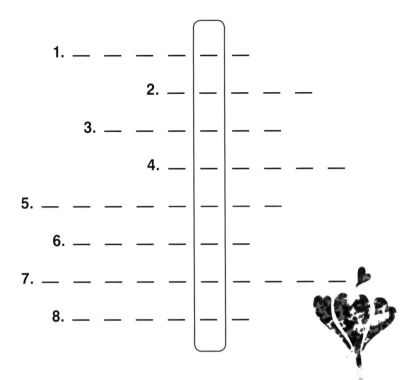

1. — — — — | — —
2. — | — — — —
3. — — — | — —
4. — | — — — —
5. — — — — — | — —
6. — — — — | —
7. — — — — — | — — — —
8. — — — — | — —

THINK ABOUT THIS...

Calliope was one of the nine Muses, that is one of the nine inspirational deities that protected the arts and letters. Calliope was the Muse of epic poetry, meaning songs and poems that praised the valiant deeds of heroes and warriors.

The other Muses were:

Clio, Euterpe, Erato, Melpomene, Polyhymnia, Terpsichore, Thalia, and Urania.

▶ An ancient artist portrays on the vase below Orpheus singing while surrounded by people of Thrace.

● How does the artist present the audience of the famous singer (facial expressions, body postures)? What is the artist trying to convey?

Berlin, National Museum

▶ Take a good look at the relief below, which tells the myth of Orpheus and Euridice.
● Write down who is who.
● What kind of emotions are the two figures on the right expressing?

------------- ------------- -------------

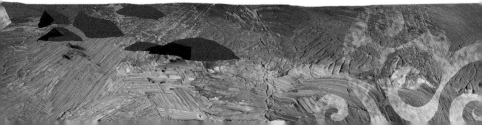

▶ The tale of Orpheus and Euridice is a tale about music and the power of love. Orpheus's love for Euridice inspires him to sing magnificently, and his music also gives him a perfect way to express his love for his sweetheart.

Music and love can be so strong that they can even beat death.

● Look up on the internet, or anywhere else you want, the lyrics to your favourite love song.
Or what about taking a go at writing your own love song?

▶ According to the myth, Orpheus longed to see his beloved Euridice so much that he turned to glance at her before they came out into the sunlight. By doing that he broke the one condition that Pluto had set and lost her forever.

● What would have happened if Orpheus had restrained himself and hadn't disobeyed Pluto's command? Write down your own version of how the tale of Orpheus and Euridice could have ended.

....
....
....
....
....
....
....
....

▶ Feel free to draw the pair of lovebirds as you see them in your imagination.

**Sandra
Eleftheriou**

Sandra Eleftheriou lives and works in Larnaca, Cyprus. She is married and has two daughters. She studied graphic design and has been working as a children's books illustrator since 2004. She has illustrated and edited more than 50 books. In 2008 & 2009 she won first prize for illustration in the Annual Competition organised by the Cypriot Association of Children's and Young Adult Books. In 2009, 2010, and 2013, she won the State Prize for Illustration by the Ministry of Education and Culture of Cyprus. Sandra also represented Cyprus on the IBBY 2012 Honour List. She is also an acclaimed writer. More information at: sandraeleftheriou.webs.com & www.facebook.com/sandraikones

Calliope Kyrdi was born and raised in Athens. She is a primary school teacher, and has written children's books, school and educational books. She likes to read, take strolls by the sea, play with cats, and chat with children. She also loves listening to myths, fairytales, and stories. Stories told by people and stories told in books.

Calliope Kyrdi

TALES FROM THE GREEK MYTHS
SERIES

Maria Angelidou

The Cattle of Geryon

Illustrated by
Iris Samartzi

ΜΕΤΑΙΧΜΙΟ

TALES FROM THE GREEK MYTHS

Maria Angelidou

The Apples of the Hesperides

Illustrated by
Iris Samartzi

ΜΕΤΑΙΧΜΙΟ

TALES FROM THE GREEK MYTHS

Maria Angelidou

The Girdle of Hippolyta

Illustrated by
Iris Samartzi

ΜΕΤΑΙΧΜΙΟ

TALES FROM THE GREEK MYTHS

Maria Angelidou

The Capture of Cerberus

Illustrated by
Iris Samartzi

ΜΕΤΑΙΧΜΙΟ

TALES FROM THE GREEK MYTHS

Maria Angelidou

The Lernaean Hydra

Illustrated by
Iris Samartzi

ΜΕΤΑΙΧΜΙΟ

TALES FROM THE GREEK MYTHS

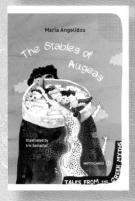

Maria Angelidou

The Stables of Augeas

Illustrated by
Iris Samartzi

ΜΕΤΑΙΧΜΙΟ

TALES FROM THE GREEK MYTHS

Kostas Poulos

The Riddle of the Sphinx

Illustrated by
Sofia Papadopoulou

ΜΕΤΑΙΧΜΙΟ

TALES FROM THE GREEK MYTHS

Kostas Poulos

The Song of the Sirens

Illustrated by
Sofia Papadopoulou

ΜΕΤΑΙΧΜΙΟ

TALES FROM THE GREEK MYTHS

www.metaixmio.gr

Kostas Poulos

The Minotaur and the Labyrinth

Illustrated by Sofia Papadopoulou

TALES FROM THE GREEK MYTHS

Kostas Poulos

I Am the Goddess Athena

Illustrated by Sofia Papadopoulou

TALES FROM THE GREEK MYTHS

Kostas Poulos

I Am the God Poseidon

Illustrated by Sofia Papadopoulou

TALES FROM THE GREEK MYTHS

Kostas Poulos

I Am the God Hermes

Illustrated by Sofia Papadopoulou

TALES FROM THE GREEK MYTHS

Kostas Poulos

I Am the Goddess Aphrodite

Illustrated by Sofia Papadopoulou

TALES FROM THE GREEK MYTHS

Antonis Papatheodoulou

The Myth of Arachne

Illustrated by Vassilis Grivas

TALES FROM THE GREEK MYTHS

Antonis Papatheodoulou

Callisto and the Book of the Sky

Illustrator: Vassilis Grivas

TALES FROM THE GREEK MYTHS

Kalliope Kyrdi

Orpheus and Eurydice

Illustrated by Sandra Eleftheriou

TALES FROM THE GREEK MYTHS